Me, Myself, and I!

Poems Selected by
Lee Bennett Hopkins

Sadlier-Oxford
A Division of William H. Sadlier, Inc.

Dear Girls and Boys,

It's great that I'm me. It's great that you're you. Both you and I are special because we are who we are.

Me, Myself, **and I!** is a book of poems about each and every one of us. I wrote one of the poems myself and I chose the others—just for you.

Enjoy the poems. Enjoy being you.

Happy Poetry-ing!

Lee Bennett Hopkins

and

Royal Dude

Contents

Birthday Song

At last comes a morning
 when nothing is wrong—
When nothing is ragged,
 or tattered, or torn—
A lollipop morning
 all slick with sweet licks,
When clouds swim in rivers,
 bugs balance on sticks,
And even the turtles
 attempt some high kicks—
It's my birth happy morning,
My happy birth day,
My Hello-to-the-World,
My Happy Hooray!

Patricia Hubbell

5

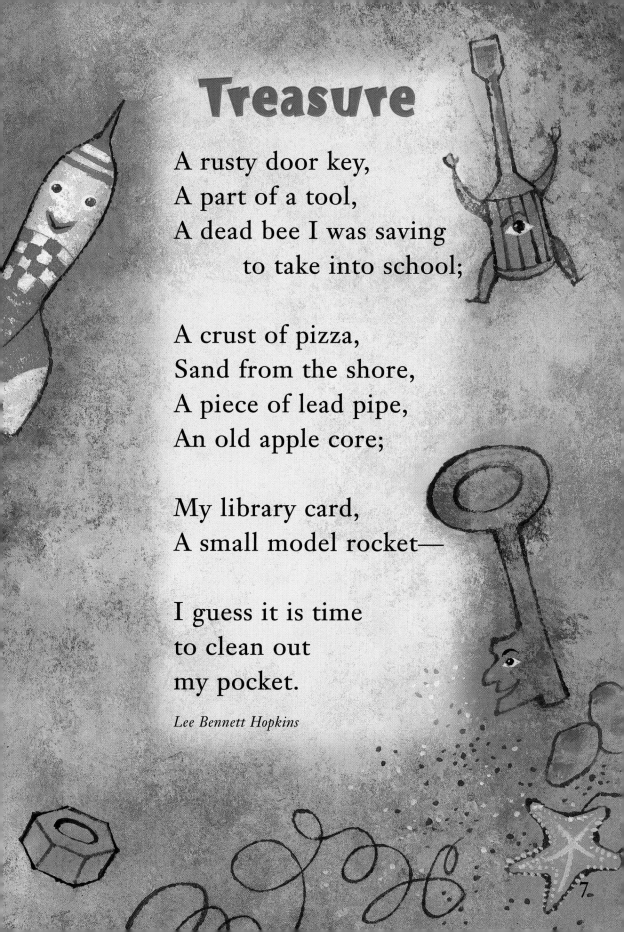

Treasure

A rusty door key,
A part of a tool,
A dead bee I was saving
        to take into school;

A crust of pizza,
Sand from the shore,
A piece of lead pipe,
An old apple core;

My library card,
A small model rocket—

I guess it is time
to clean out
my pocket.

Lee Bennett Hopkins

Time to Play

Mama says to play outside.
Wish I had a bike to ride.
I'll fly to the moon instead.
Steer the rocket in my head.
I'll pretend to find a star
no one else has seen so far.
Then I'll name it after me—

Africa Lawanda Lee!

But for now I'll grab some chalk,
play hopscotch out on the walk.

Nikki Grimes

Ice Cream Cone

Strawberry ice cream
cold and sweet;
sugar cone
my favorite treat!

Pink and sticky
melting drips;
I lick it off
my finger tips!

Heidi E.Y. Stemple

9

A Circle of Sun

I'm dancing.
I'm leaping.
I'm skipping about.
I gallop.
I grin.
I giggle.
I shout.
I'm earth's many colors.
I'm morning and night.
I'm honey on toast.
I'm funny.
I'm bright.
I'm swinging.
I'm singing.
I wiggle.
I run.
I'm a piece of the sky
in a circle of sun.

Rebecca Kai Dotlich

To Miss Michele's
class
Rebecca Kai Dotlich

FIRST BOOK

Mommy! Daddy!
Come look, come look—

I'm reading, I'm reading,
I'm reading a book!

I just found it here
on the library shelf
and I can read every word
all by myself.

Mommy! Daddy!
Come look, come look—

I'm reading!

I'm reading
my very first book!

Linda Kulp

13

BEST FRIENDS

I like you and
you like me
we
will always be—
best friends.

Playing together
or watching TV,
we
like each other's
company.

Best friends
we
will always be—
because
I like you and
you like me!

Linda Kulp

Wishes

I jump off a pier.
Swim 'till late night.

Catch fireflies flitting in
Late-August flight.

I sit.

I dream
On a star beaming bright—

I make wonder-filled wishes
This midsummer night.

Tom Robert Shields